# See the Seasons

Written by
Rozanne Lanczak Williams

**Harcourt**

Orlando   Boston   Dallas   Chicago   San Diego

**www.harcourtschool.com**

What can you see?

2

What can you see?

What can you see?

Can you see me?

## Teacher/Family Member

Have your child keep track of the weather for a week on a calendar. He or she should draw small pictures in the squares for sun, rain, wind, and snow. Ask your child to suggest clothing to wear for the weather.

**High-Frequency Words:** *what, see*

**Word Count:** 16

Photo Credits

Key: (t), top; (b), bottom; (c), center; (l), left; (r), right; (bkgd), background.

Front cover: (daisies), Craig Tuttle / The Stock Market; (ocean), Claudia Kunin / Tony Stone Images; (sunflowers), Philip H. Coblentz / Tony Stone Images; (winter), Craig Tuttle / The Stock Market. Page 2-3, Camerique / The Picture Cube; 2(inset), Bob Thomas / Tony Stone Images; 3(inset), Jim Strawser / Grant Heilman Photography; 4, Claudia Kunin / Tony Stone Images; 4-5, Craig Tuttle / The Stock Market; 6-7, Philip H. Coblentz / Tony Stone Images, 6(inset), Elena Reoraid / PhotoEdit; 7(inset), Lori Adamski Peek / Tony Stone Images; 8, Curt Maas / Tony Stone Images; 8(inset), Randy Duchaine / The Stock Market. Back cover (tl), Craig Tuttle / The Stock Market; (tr), Claudia Kunin / Tony Stone Images; (bl), Philip H. Coblentz / Tony Stone Images; (br), Craig Tuttle / The Stock Market.

Printed in the United States of America

Grade K  Book 4     ISBN 0-15-314845-4

Ordering Options:     0-15-316196-5     Package of 5
                      0-15-316225-2     Grade K Package, Books 1-6

6  7  8  9  10    179    2001  00

Instant Readers
Science

Harcourt

K Book 4

0-15-314845-4

9 780153 148453

90000 >

# The Garden

By Veronica Freeman Ellis

Illustrated by Holly Cooper

# THIS BOOK IS THE PROPERTY OF:

STATE _____
PROVINCE _____
COUNTY _____
PARISH _____
SCHOOL DISTRICT _____
OTHER _____

Book No. _____
Enter information
in spaces
to the left as
instructed.

| ISSUED TO | Year Used | CONDITION | |
|-----------|-----------|-----------|----------|
| | | ISSUED | RETURNED |
| _____ | _____ | _____ | _____ |
| _____ | _____ | _____ | _____ |
| _____ | _____ | _____ | _____ |
| _____ | _____ | _____ | _____ |
| _____ | _____ | _____ | _____ |
| _____ | _____ | _____ | _____ |
| _____ | _____ | _____ | _____ |
| _____ | _____ | _____ | _____ |

**PUPILS to whom this textbook is issued must not write on any page or mark any part of it in any way, consumable textbooks excepted.**

1. Teachers should see that the pupil's name is clearly written in ink in the spaces above in every book issued.
2. The following terms should be used in recording the condition of the book: New; Good; Fair; Poor; Bad.